STICKER ADVENTURES

How to use this book

Read the captions, then find the sticker that best fits the space. (Hint: check the sticker labels for clues!)

•

There are lots of fantastic extra stickers for creating your own scenes throughout the book.

Penguin Random House

Written by Gaurav Joshi
Edited by Emma Grange, Simon Hugo, Clare Millar, and Chitra Subramanyam
Designed by David McDonald and Pranika Jain
Jacket designed by Mark Penfound
DTP Designers Umesh Singh Rawat, Rajdeep Singh

For Lucasfilm
Executive Editor Jonathan W. Rinzler
Art Director Troy Alders
Story Group Rayne Roberts, Pablo Hidalgo, Leland Chee

This updated edition published in 2018
First American Edition, 2015
Published in the United States by DK Publishing
345 Hudson Street, New York, New York 10014
DK, a Division of Penguin Random House LLC

Page design copyright © 2018 Dorling Kindersley Limited.

001–310945–Oct/2018

A catalog record for this book is available from the Library of Congress.

ISBN: 978-1-4654-7657-9

Printed and bound in China

www.LEGO.com
www.starwars.com
www.dk.com

A WORLD OF IDEAS:
SEE ALL THERE IS TO KNOW

EVIL FORCES

Beware the villains that haunt the galaxy! Some make no secret of their plans to destroy planets and people. But the most dangerous are the evil Sith and the First Order. These enemies of peace will stop at nothing to rule the galaxy.

DARTH SIDIOUS

The Sith Lord's dark powers make him the most powerful villain in the galaxy. Who is he? His voice seems so familiar.

DARTH VADER

Vader used to be a famous Jedi. Tempted by the Sith, he turned evil. He can choke his foes without touching them.

BOBA FETT

This cunning bounty hunter works for some of the biggest villains in the galaxy, finding people and even destroying them. No one can escape Boba Fett.

CAPTAIN PHASMA

Captain Phasma leads the stormtroopers in the First Order. She wears shiny silver armor that shows her rank. You wouldn't want to fight her—she is deadly!

GENERAL GRIEVOUS

This savage cyborg terrorizes his foes with his brilliant combat skills. Watch out for his four lightsabers!

JABBA THE HUTT

Slimy and wrinkly, Jabba is one of the most feared crime lords in the galaxy. He loves watching his enemies being eaten by monsters. Ugh!

DARTH MAUL

Beware this mysterious warrior and his double-bladed lightsaber. He wants to destroy all the Jedi.

KYLO REN

Kylo Ren is the First Order's greatest warrior. He uses the dark side of the Force and wants to rule the galaxy. Will anyone be able to stop this formidable fighter?

SUPREME LEADER SNOKE

Snoke is the leader of the First Order. His base is a huge Mega-Destroyer starship. Snoke is skilled in the dark side of the Force. He uses the Force to try and control the galaxy.

MIGHTY HEROES

Meet the brave heroes that battle to restore peace to the galaxy. They are not afraid to fight back with help from their friends and allies. From Jedi to smugglers, these heroes will never stop trying to defeat the evil forces of the galaxy.

DROID PROTECTION
Two droids, C-3PO and R2-D2, are always ready to help Luke Skywalker. They have rescued him from many sticky situations.

YODA
Never underestimate Yoda. The leader of the Jedi Council may be 900 years old and a little on the small size, but he is all-powerful.

REY
Rey is strong with the Force. She wants to use the light side of the Force and hopes she can help the Resistance restore peace.

POE DAMERON
Poe is the best pilot in the Resistance. He will do everything he can to defeat the evil First Order that threatens the galaxy.

ANAKIN SKYWALKER
Anakin is one of the greatest Jedi Knights. Yet, there is something dark about him. Is he really a good guy?

PADMÉ AMIDALA
The Queen of Naboo just wants peace in the galaxy. Give her a blaster though, and she is ready to fight for her people.

HAN SOLO
This smuggler has been known to meddle with scary crime lords. He is an unlikely hero who is always ready to battle evil villains.

LUKE SKYWALKER
He may have started his Jedi training a little late, but the Force is strong in Luke Skywalker. He is determined to destroy the evil Sith.

PRINCESS LEIA
Bad guys, beware! Leia is one of the galaxy's greatest and bravest heroes. She thinks she has no time for scoundrels like Han Solo!

CHEWBACCA
This Wookiee may look cuddly, but watch out. Chewie is a fearsome, super-tall warrior with a very short temper.

STRIFE ON NABOO

The evil Sith will try anything to gain control of the galaxy. They use the Trade Federation to invade the planet of Naboo. The Sith believe that this will scare people into giving up their freedom. All this will keep the Jedi very, very busy.

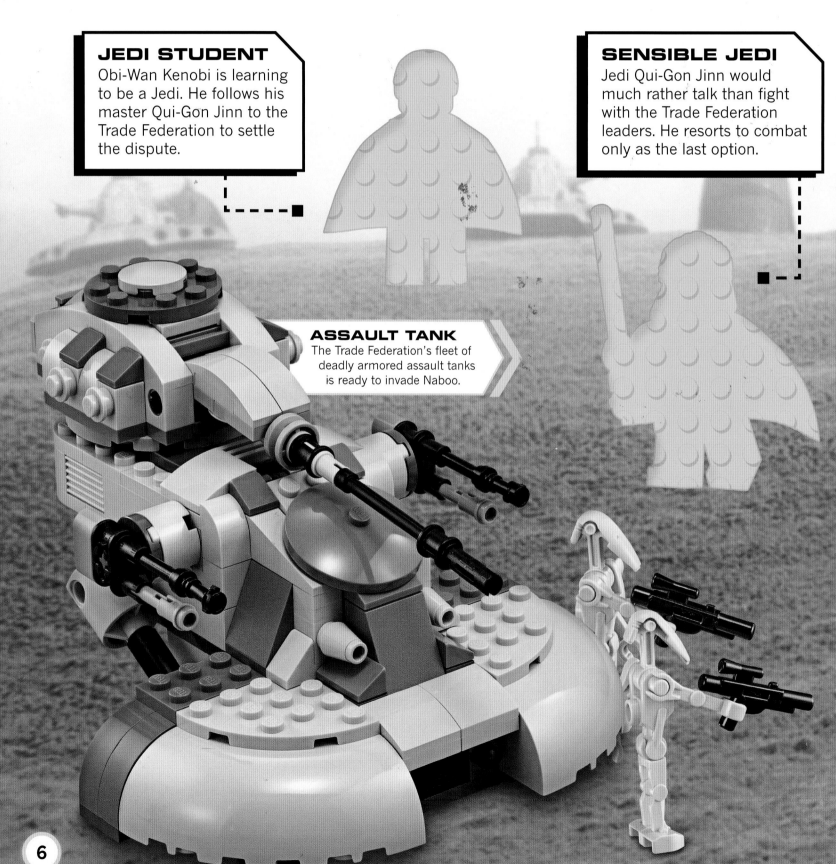

JEDI STUDENT
Obi-Wan Kenobi is learning to be a Jedi. He follows his master Qui-Gon Jinn to the Trade Federation to settle the dispute.

SENSIBLE JEDI
Jedi Qui-Gon Jinn would much rather talk than fight with the Trade Federation leaders. He resorts to combat only as the last option.

ASSAULT TANK
The Trade Federation's fleet of deadly armored assault tanks is ready to invade Naboo.

NABOO QUEEN
Padmé makes sure she looks like a queen when she asks for help to stop the invasion on her home planet, Naboo. But will anybody listen to her?

EVIL SITH
Darth Maul has only one thing on his mind. He wants to destroy Padmé because she is interfering with his Master's plans.

PILOT BATTLE DROID
The Trade Federation deploys thousands of skilled pilot droids to operate combat vehicles. They are ready to strike Naboo.

JAR JAR BINKS
Clumsy Jar Jar ends up defending his home planet of Naboo. Armed with a spear and a shield, he is afraid to go into battle.

WATTO
Watto is a junkyard dealer on Tatooine. A young boy called Anakin is his slave. He doesn't want Anakin to travel to Naboo and fight with the Jedi.

YOUNG ANAKIN
Anakin is a brave podracer. He shows promise of becoming a great Jedi. Qui-Gon wants Anakin as his student Padawan.

BATTLE ON NABOO
Naboo was once peaceful. But not anymore. Help the Jedi stop the Trade Federation droid ships before it's too late.

Use the extra stickers to create your own scene on Naboo.

SECRET SITH ARMY

A divided galaxy is easier to control. The more the planets fight with each other, the easier it is for Darth Sidious to become Emperor. And a secret army of clones is sure to help, too! It's the perfect plan. Will the Jedi ever discover the truth?

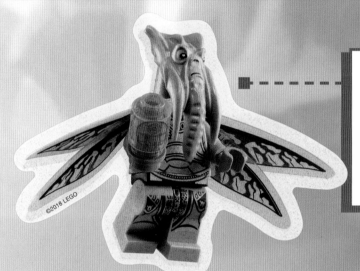

SLY DOOKU

The mysterious Dooku is a Sith Lord. He secretly creates an army. His Force Lightning attack is perfect for paralyzing his foes. Bzzt!

POGGLE THE LESSER

The elaborate prints on Poggle's robe show that he is royalty. This Geonosian leader helps Dooku with his evil plans.

PADAWAN ANAKIN

Anakin is still a student but he is very proud of his lightsaber skills. He thinks he is ready to face Dooku.

MACE WINDU

This Jedi Master has seen many battles. Years of experience have taught him to not underestimate the dark forces.

BATTLE READY

Padmé can fight in a battle just as well as any Jedi. She is an ace shot with her blaster pistol. Watch out, Dooku!

JANGO FETT

Jango's genes are copied to create a clone army. This ruthless bounty hunter wears blue Mandalorian armor and carries deadly blaster guns.

WISE LEADER

Yoda takes control of the clone army. But can it really be used as a force for good?

FOLLOWING ORDERS

Under the helmet, all clone troopers look like Jango Fett. They carry blaster guns and are programmed to just follow orders without question.

POWER STRUGGLE

The Jedi use the clone army to win battles—but the Sith are always ready to start more. Both sides struggle to build up their armies in order to defeat the other. The galaxy has been plunged into the Clone Wars.

AHSOKA TANO
The Jedi discovered Ahsoka when she was a little girl. This brave Padawan can hunt down even the most dangerous enemies.

NEW ROLE
Anakin has a new task at hand. He has to train Ahsoka to be a Jedi. He takes her on many of his adventures.

JEDI GENERAL
Years of experience have made Obi-Wan a skilled diplomat. He tries to convince everyone to settle disputes peacefully.

CAPTAIN REX
Unlike other clone troopers, Rex can actually think for himself. He wears a special helmet with breathing filters on either side.

PLO KOON
This Jedi general can face any challenge thrown at him with courage. Just don't ask him to remove his mask. He can't breathe without it.

PONG KRELL

Few can match the combat skills of this Jedi Master. Pong uses his four arms to attack with double-bladed lightsabers.

CAD BANE

This bounty hunter works for the biggest villains in the galaxy—from Dooku to Darth Sidious. For money, he will even hunt down his friends.

SECOND LIFE

Everyone thought that Darth Maul was destroyed for good. Watch out! He's back—and this time with stronger mechanical legs.

COMMANDO DROID

The Sith use these menacing BX-series droid commandos for stealth missions.

SITH ASSAULT

The galaxy has been betrayed. Chancellor Palpatine—the man everyone had trusted—has revealed himself to be the fearsome Darth Sidious. He has even turned a powerful Jedi to evil. It's time for the dark side of the Force to rise.

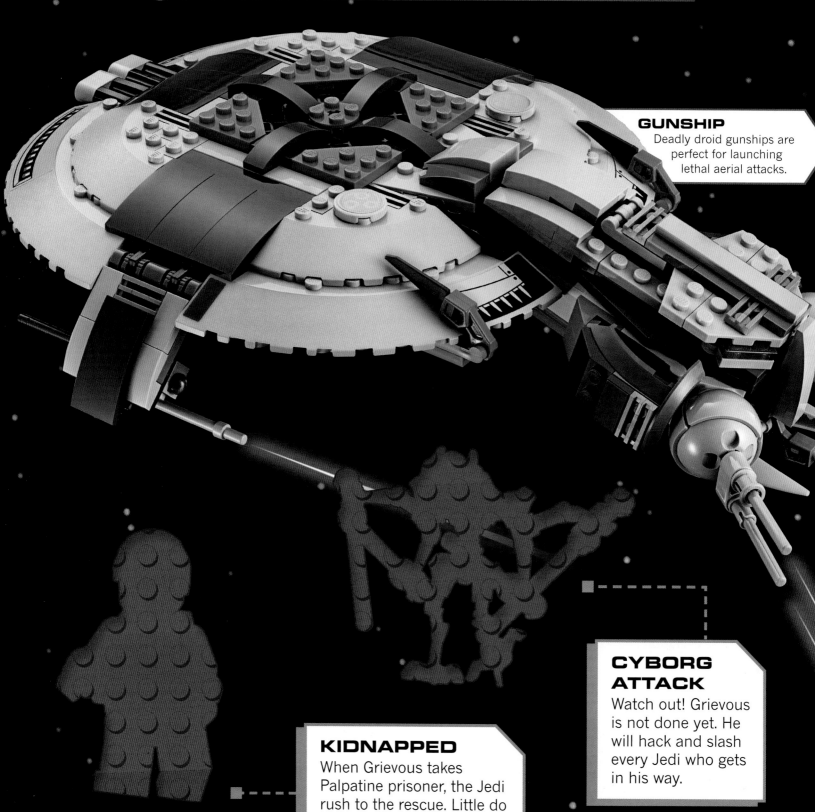

GUNSHIP
Deadly droid gunships are perfect for launching lethal aerial attacks.

CYBORG ATTACK
Watch out! Grievous is not done yet. He will hack and slash every Jedi who gets in his way.

KIDNAPPED
When Grievous takes Palpatine prisoner, the Jedi rush to the rescue. Little do they know that it's all part of Palpatine's clever plan.

OBI-WAN'S TASK

Obi-Wan knows that the Sith are up to no good. He must protect the Jedi Order from falling apart.

HAIRY GIANT

The Jedi are lucky to have Chewbacca on their side. Chewie is a fearless fighter. Watch out for his bowcaster.

CRUSHED

This unfortunate battle droid thought he could take on the Wookiee chief Tarfful. But he is no match for Tarfful's strength.

COMMANDER GREE

This commander works with the Jedi. Armed with a blaster and a pair of macrobinoculars, he is ready to take on the droids.

SHARP SHOOTER

Neimoidian warriors serve the army fighting the Republic. Their weapons can do some major damage.

JEDI NO MORE

Anakin could not resist the temptations of the dark side of the Force. He becomes Sidious's apprentice, Darth Vader.

MIGHTY BATTLES

When a fierce Jedi and a ferocious Sith come face to face, a deadly duel is sure to follow. In a battle of the mighty, only the strongest, bravest, and most cunning survive. There's no room for error. Good luck, fighters!

GRIEVOUS VS. OBI-WAN
Grievous is super fast and has many secret weapons. But the menacing cyborg is no match for Obi-Wan's skills and bravery.

YOU'RE UNDER ARREST CHANCELLOR!

ANAKIN VS. DOOKU

Anakin lost his arm when he last fought Dooku. This time he is hungry for revenge. Watch out, Count Dooku!

QUI-GON VS. MAUL

Darth Maul thinks he is indestructible. But he hasn't met Qui-Gon yet. The brave Jedi Master is not afraid of anything and will fight Maul.

ARE YOU THREATENING ME, MASTER JEDI?

GOOD VS. EVIL

Mace Windu wants to arrest Palpatine for plotting against the galaxy. He doesn't know about the Chancellor's Sith powers.

HIDE AND ATTACK

Challenging the Empire is not easy, but a Rebel Alliance has been formed to fight against it. Darth Vader is preparing the Empire's deadliest weapon yet—the Death Star. Can the rebels save the galaxy from this planet-destroying menace?

BRAVE PRINCESS

The Empire destroyed Leia's planet and she will not stop until she restores democracy. Watch out, Vader!

FARMER LUKE

Luke Skywalker lives a boring life on Tatooine. He is eager for adventure. How about saving the galaxy from the Sith?

BEN KENOBI

Mysterious Ben Kenobi has a secret. He was once a Jedi who fought in the Clone Wars. Now it's time to come out of hiding.

BRAVE WOOKIEE

Chewbacca is Han's best pal. He looks out for his buddy and protects him from danger. This Wookiee is a true friend.

ACE PILOT

The rebels could use a good pilot like Han. But the handsome smuggler will only fight for money. Unless Leia asks nicely!

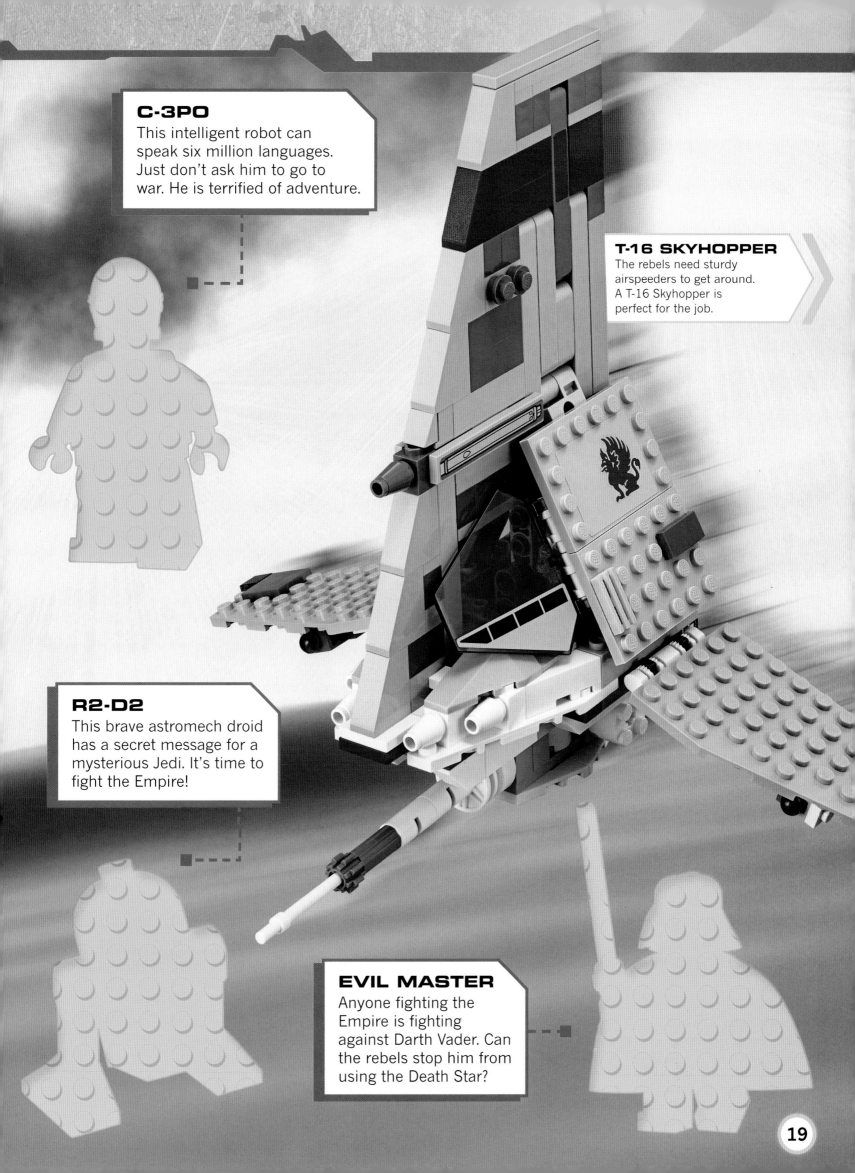

C-3PO

This intelligent robot can speak six million languages. Just don't ask him to go to war. He is terrified of adventure.

T-16 SKYHOPPER

The rebels need sturdy airspeeders to get around. A T-16 Skyhopper is perfect for the job.

R2-D2

This brave astromech droid has a secret message for a mysterious Jedi. It's time to fight the Empire!

EVIL MASTER

Anyone fighting the Empire is fighting against Darth Vader. Can the rebels stop him from using the Death Star?

SITH FIGHT BACK

The rebels can't hide from Darth Vader forever—he always hunts them down. With the Death Star destroyed, the evil Sith Lord is more furious than ever. It's time for Luke and his gang to prepare for action. The war is far from over!

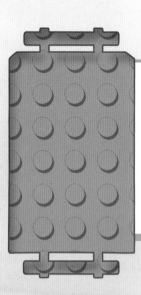

FROZEN HAN

Darth Vader doesn't go easy on his enemies. He freezes Han Solo in carbonite and hands him over to Boba Fett. Jabba the Hutt will be very happy.

POWERFUL TEACHER

Yoda feels that Luke is too old to be trained. But the wise Jedi Master knows how to teach a student like Luke.

REBEL TROOPER

A rebel trooper just needs a blaster rifle to face the Imperial forces. These soldiers love a good fight.

GENERAL RIEEKAN

The rebels are lucky to have this brave general on their side. Rieekan will risk his life to protect the galaxy.

GENERAL VEERS

This ruthless general of the Imperial Army is very efficient. He destroys the shield generator so Darth Vader can attack the rebels.

BOUNTY HUNTER
Bounty hunter Boba is just as ruthless as his father, Jango Fett. He is out to capture Han for a huge bounty from Jabba the Hutt.

TIE PILOT
Skilled pilots fly the TIE fighters for the Imperial Army. They wear scary black helmets and are armed with deadly weapons.

UNLUCKY LUKE
Luke is one of the leaders of the Rebel Alliance, dedicated to fighting evil. He is shocked to find out that Darth Vader is actually his father.

AT-AT WALKERS
These war machines of the Imperial Army are perfect for shooting down enemy vehicles.

BATTLE OF HOTH

Help Luke Skywalker and the rebel trooper fight the imperial soldiers on Hoth. Be careful! It can get very cold.

Use the extra stickers to create your own scene on Hoth.

GALAXY HANGOUT

Welcome to Mos Eisley Cantina. This saloon is known for its loud music and dangerous fights. It's a great place to hold meetings and discuss secret missions. It's also the coolest hangout for criminals and brave pilots alike.

BITH MUSICIANS

These skilled musicians entertain the customers of the Cantina. All band members wear matching outfits.

SMART SMUGGLER

Han Solo keeps a blaster handy in case a bounty hunter comes looking for him. This smuggler-pilot also has a fast ship for hire.

LOOKING FOR A RIDE

It's time to leave Tatooine and fight the Empire. But Luke can't do it in his landspeeder. He needs a fast ship and a skilled pilot.

CAREFUL BEN

Ben Kenobi knows he could run into a few criminals at the Mos Eisley Cantina. He carries his lightsaber with him, just in case.

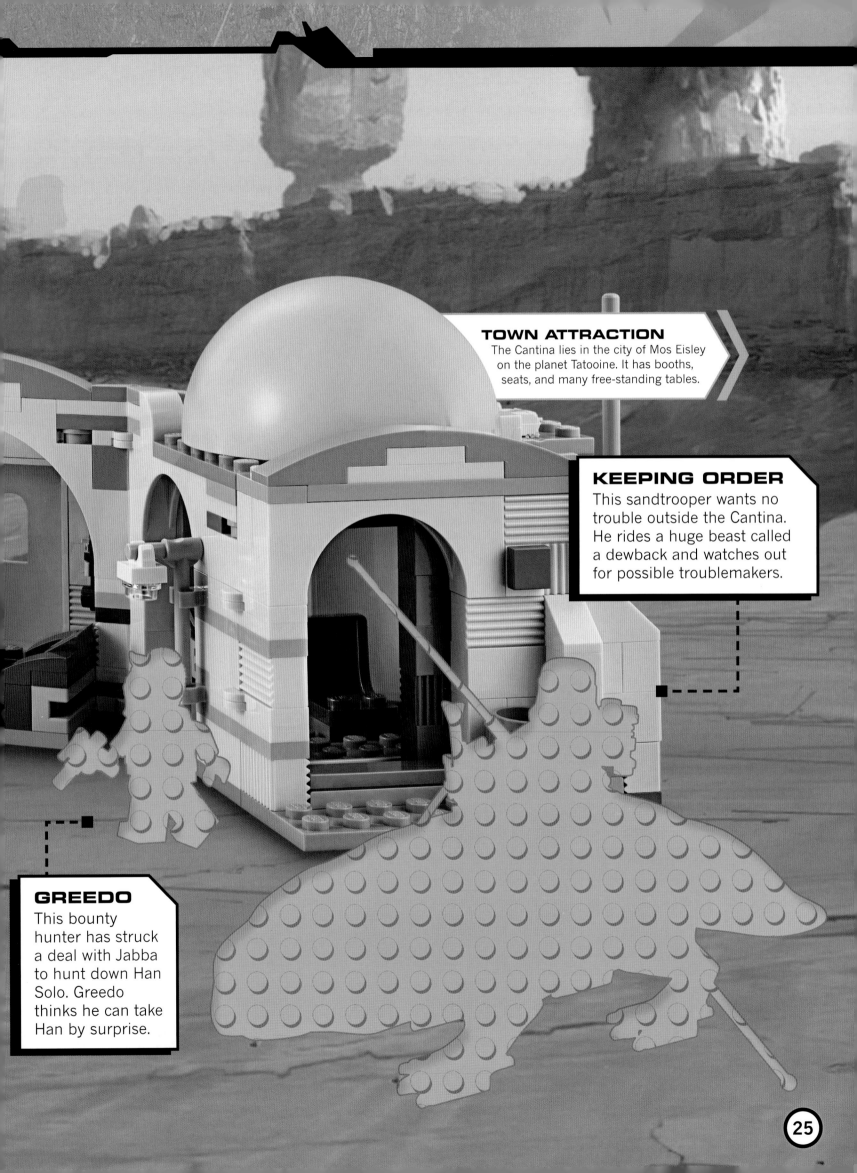

TOWN ATTRACTION
The Cantina lies in the city of Mos Eisley on the planet Tatooine. It has booths, seats, and many free-standing tables.

KEEPING ORDER
This sandtrooper wants no trouble outside the Cantina. He rides a huge beast called a dewback and watches out for possible troublemakers.

GREEDO
This bounty hunter has struck a deal with Jabba to hunt down Han Solo. Greedo thinks he can take Han by surprise.

END OF VADER

The rebels are more determined than ever to put an end to the Empire's rule. The Force is strong with the Jedi once again. Not even the threat of a new Death Star will stop them. Luke and his rebel friends are ready to strike. Beware, Darth Vader!

BOUSHH

Watch out! There's another bounty hunter on the prowl. But it's really Princess Leia in disguise to save Han Solo from Jabba.

LANDO CALRISSIAN

Lando is a smuggler and an old pal of Han Solo. He heads to Tatooine to rescue his friend. Hang on, Han!

VENGEFUL JABBA

Nothing gives slimy Jabba more pleasure than torturing his foes. He thinks that a frozen Han Solo makes for a great wall hanging.

FREE AGAIN

Han is a free man again—his friends have destroyed Jabba. He heads to the forest moon of Endor to blow up the Empire's new Death Star.

EWOKS

The rebels find unexpected friends on the moon of Endor. The Ewoks may be small but they are not scared of Vader's army of stormtroopers.

DEFEATED

Palpatine thought that he could turn Luke into a Sith. But Luke is a true Jedi. He battles the evil Emperor and foils his plans.

EMPIRE'S END

Faced with a choice between his son and the Emperor, Darth Vader chooses to put an end to his evil Master. He sacrifices himself to bring balance to the Force.

FORGIVENESS

Luke battles Vader, but forgives him in the end. The light side of the Force has won.

REBELS RISING

Since the fall of the evil Empire many years ago, the surviving Imperials have been plotting their revenge. They have named themselves the First Order. The Resistance must rise once again to battle for the peace of the galaxy.

REY

Rey has lived alone on Jakku for many years. She is a scavenger. When she rescues Resistance droid, BB-8, her life changes forever.

KYLO REN

Kylo Ren is very powerful. He is determined to destroy the Resistance. Will Rey and the others be able to stop him?

FIRST ORDER

The First Order is a dangerous organization. Its evil leaders want to take control of the galaxy.

BB-8

BB-8 is an astromech droid. He helps his friend, Poe Dameron, fly his X-wing.

LUGGABEAST

A Teedo scavenger rides this creature called a luggabeast. They try and capture BB-8— Rey comes to the rescue!

STORM-TROOPER

Stormtroopers are the First Order's army of highly skilled soldiers. They have strong armor and carry powerful weapons.

HAN SOLO

Han was a smuggler who joined the rebels and fell in love with General Leia. Since the war, Han has gone back to smuggling.

POE DAMERON

Poe is the bravest pilot in the Resistance. General Leia has sent him on a mission to help find her brother, Luke, who has not been seen for many years.

UNKAR PLUTT

Unkar is a mean junk dealer on Jakku. Rey takes what she can scavenge and sells it to Unkar in exchange for food.

FIRST ORDER TIE FIGHTER

TIE fighters are the First Order's main attack vehicles. They are fast and dangerous—only the best TIE fighter pilots are allowed to fly them.

KYLO'S SHUTTLE

This elite shuttle transports Kylo Ren across the galaxy. It can attack enemy starfighters.

FINN

Finn was once a stormtrooper. He sees how evil the First Order is, and, with Poe's help, runs away.

GALAXY AT WAR!

The galaxy is at war once again. Supreme Leader Snoke rules the First Order and seeks to destroy the Resistance. While Finn and Rose try to sneak aboard Snoke's Mega-Destroyer, Rey learns to use the Force. Will they defeat they First Order?

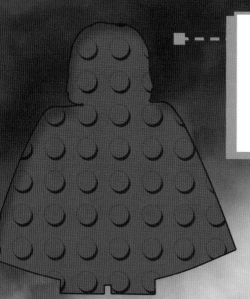

KYLO REN
Kylo Ren is General Leia's son but Kylo does not speak to his family. He is strong with the dark side of the Force and wants to defeat the Resistance.

LEIA ORGANA
Brave General Leia is the founder of the Resistance. She has fought in many battles during her life. Can she bring her fleet to safety?

POE DAMERON
Poe often gets into trouble for not following orders. Poe respects General Leia but does not trust Vice Admiral Holdo.

REY
When Rey discovers she is strong with the Force, she is eager to learn how to use it. She seeks out the last surviving Jedi on a planet called Ahch-To.

VICE ADMIRAL HOLDO
When Leia is injured Vice Admiral Holdo becomes the leader of the Resistance. Holdo must work hard to bring the fleet out of danger.

ESCAPE TIME

This small, agile shuttle is used by Finn and Rose to depart the Resistance fleet without being detected.

LUKE SKYWALKER

Luke is the last Jedi and the brother of General Leia. Rey finds him on Ahch-To and asks him to teach her how to use the Force.

ROSE TICO

Rose works as a technician for the Resistance. She repairs starfighters when they are damaged in battle. She wants to defeat the First Order!

FINN

Having escaped the First Order, Finn is now a Resistance fighter. Rose and Finn must work together on a mission.

HEAVY ASSAULT WALKER

These huge walkers have space inside for transporting troops. They tower over their enemies on the ground—watch out!

GALAXY'S PEOPLE

The galaxy is home to many different creatures. Some help the Jedi or Sith in their battles. Others contribute to galaxy life in everyday ways. From skilled musicians to criminals on the run, these characters make life in the galaxy very exciting.

REE-YEES
A native from a planet called Kinyen, Ree-Yees is a criminal. He has made a lot of enemies on his home planet. He now lives on Tatooine.

PORG
Fluffy little porgs live on the planet Ahch-To. They are curious and friendly. They are bird-like and roost in cliffs.

TREADWELL DROID
These repair droids can fix just about anything. They have multiple mechanical hands and tools to help them with repairs.

JAWA
These tiny natives of Tatooine will sell anything they can steal and savage. They once sold C-3PO and R2-D2 to Luke's uncle, Owen Lars.

ROYAL GUARD
Never mess with the guards of Emperor Palpatine. They are loyal to the Dark Lord and will defend him to the death.